Dialogical Psychiatry

*A Handbook For The Teaching &
Practice Of Open Dialogue*

By

Russell Razzaque

Omni House Press

Acknowledgments

My first thanks, as always, must go to my family. I juggle far too many things in my life, now so more than ever, and it is their endless understanding, acceptance and support that makes it all possible.

Jaakko Seikkula is the other person I'd like to especially thank, for his teaching, advice and guidance over the years. I'm particularly grateful for his review of this book and helpful input into my final draft.

Finally, I'd like to thank all the trainers, trainees, managers, clients and families - national and international - who have joined us in our quest to bring Open Dialogue to the UK and indeed the world. We have taken the first steps together. There is a long road ahead, but the hardest part of a journey is often making a start. And thanks to you, we now have.

Contents

Please note: This book is not a substitute for formal Open Dialogue training. No book is. Training in Open Dialogue is a deeply experiential endeavour and, just as it is not possible to learn to swim solely in a classroom, so one cannot learn the practice of Open Dialogue solely from a book.

More Than Meds

What makes the difference for your patients? What is it that you do that really helps them the most? For most of us – psychiatrists, social workers, OTs and psychiatric nurses working in the front line of mental health services today – the answer will usually centre around medication. That is seen as the primary cause of change and that's exactly what I thought for most of my professional life. The hope I had for my patients' improvement was predominantly a factor of my faith in the drug I was giving them. And if that didn't work I tried another one. Then another one. And on it went. That was my job as I saw it. When people kept coming back I tended to assume either that they were non compliant with their medication or that they just weren't on the right pill, or even cocktail, yet.

I knew that my relationship with them had some kind of impact but I wasn't very clear about what. I also knew that in almost all cases there were major life events – stressors, relationships and traumas – that played a major role in their reason for seeking help, or being referred for help, but the treatment from me and most of my team at least involved very little reference to this. That tended to be the role of a psychologist even though it would represent, at most, a small fraction of the contact and face time they were getting. For us it was all about symptoms and meds. This was how my whole community recovery team operated; the manager, the middle and junior doctors, the clinical leads, the care coordinators (a mix of nurses, social workers and OTs) and the support workers too. We were all like planets orbiting round and orientated by the central treatment resource, which was the medication.

Today those same nurses, social workers, OTs and support workers are largely still in post but the way they work – the way we all work together – couldn't be more different. Unlike before, what we realise now is that it is our relationships that really make the difference. It's what we do, how we talk, how we ask questions, who we invite in the room and even how we talk about clients outside the room that is foremost in our thinking because time and time again, we have found that that is what makes the change.

Open Dialogue developed through over a decade of trial and error in Northern Finland, where their teams engaged in a cyclical process of improvement to determine how each of these aspects of the way they work can make a difference. This came about because they knew, as we have all known for many years, that engaging people more in their own care and involving and cultivating their family and social milieu has a profound impact on long term outcomes[12]. What we never knew before them,

[1] Camice et al. (2015), *Ten Year Outcomes of First Episode Psychosis in the MRC AESOP-10 Study*. The Journal of Mental and Nervous Disease, May 2015

[2] Giacco et al. (2012), *Friends and Symptom Dimensions in Patients with Psychosis: A Pooled Analysis*. PLoS ONE, 2012

however, is exactly how to implement that in an all encompassing service model; one that could be used for all those presenting to the team with a severe mental health issue, especially when presenting in crisis.

Despite strong evidence of the efficacy of family therapy that has built up through countless studies over the years[3], in most countries, very few people actually receive it. That's because it's seen as a separate speciality altogether. You have your care from day to day and if you're offered family therapy then you'll receive that in addition to the mainstay of your treatment, like a bit of side dressing, rather

---

[3] Von Sydow et al. (2010), *The Efficacy of Systemic Therapy with Adult Patients: A Meta-Content Analysis of 38 Randomised Controlled Trials*. Family Processes, November 2010

than as the whole basis of your treatment in the first place. Attempts over the years to train individuals in family based approaches, in the hope that they might implement it in some of their work, have been met with limited success as, again, this was not an overarching culture imbibed across the whole team. Without a whole service approach, such skills rapidly wither. And where family therapy services do exist, by the time people receive it the crisis was over a long time ago. A key innovation of Open Dialogue was thus to bring it into the front line, starting at the point of crisis referral. Though some of the original papers published about it tended to focus on psychosis, the service itself was for anyone. It was fundamental to the culture of how the whole team operated and still do to this day. They all think family, systems and networks from day one.

"It seems so obvious when I think about it now," said Frank Umoh, an experienced consultant psychiatrist in Essex during an Open Dialogue training session we ran for his team in 2019. "All this time we have been taking patients out of their environment and treating them in isolation. Even when we went to their homes, we thought the care was only for them. Then after discharge we put them straight back into the same environment and, of course, usually they come back. We needed to work with that whole network to really make the change and in all this time that was never our focus." His realisation is a common one for colleagues on the training.

Working with someone's whole environment, however, doesn't come easy. It's not just a case of inviting everyone into the room. I thought, after having spent some time reading about Open Dialogue and studying some of its original papers and texts, that I understood it and that it wouldn't be too difficult for me to make the switch. But I was completely wrong. Val Jackson, now a fellow Open Dialogue trainer with me, was my tutor back in 2014 and she had to challenge me a few times to really help me appreciate the systemic perspective. Powerful exercises such as "the sculpt", as it has come to be known, help students absorb and integrate some of these core notions. This involves asking several students to act the role of family members and stand at the centre of the room. Other trainees play their friends and extended family who are then added as a story is read out involving different characters in the network. Each is asked to adjust their position in relation to the others in response to the developing storylines, depending on how the various bonds and relationships around them are affected. We start to then physically see the way in which an event that might concern one member of the network has ripple effects across the whole network. And we see how the reaction to each event depends and builds on the reaction to the last. We notice a dynamic fluid ever shifting three dimensional formation is in action, like an organism in its own right, to which each member plays but a small part. Like a flock of birds flying in a complex formation, constantly adjusting and taking their cues from one another, we humans aren't much different. How many connections do you have in your life? How many events that could occur in people one, two or even several links removed from you could nevertheless have an impact on your life and how you feel? The permutations are almost endless and yet our system for helping people in distress essentially treats them as if those connections have little or no meaning. We are all part of a system that is itself part of a wider system, and on it goes. The more we widen our horizon, when it comes to helping someone in distress, the more profound that help will be.

And, of course, the distress that we are talking about relates, in the vast majority of cases, to trauma[4567]. An array of studies in recent years have underscored the extent to which trauma, at some point in their lives, is the reason most people come into contact with mental health services. Yet, how well equipped are we to understand and possibly shift the impact of that trauma? Medication may reduce the symptoms that it creates today, but the underlying emotional distress still remains. And we generally

---

[4] Ellason & Ross (1997), *Childhood Trauma and Psychiatric Symptoms.* Psychological Reports, April 1997

[5] Read et al (2005), *Childhood Trauma, Psychosis and Schizophrenia: a Literature Review with Theoretical and Clinical Implications.* Acta Psychiatrica Scandinavia, October 2005

[6] Floen and Elklit (2007), *Psychiatric Diagnosis, Trauma and Suicidality.* Annals of General Psychiatry, April 2007

[7] Passmann et al. (2013), *The Role of Early Life Stress in Adult Psychiatric Disorders: A Systematic Review According to Childhood Trauma Subtypes.* The Journal of Nervous and Mental Disease, December 2013

don't seem to do much about it. In some respects we are like cardiologists who don't listen to the heart; as if, faced with the symptoms of acute chest pain, we treat the patient with morphine alone without any reference to the underlying cardiac cause.

Just like working with families, working with trauma also takes some training. But it can't be training or an expertise that is left to the lone psychologist in the team. It needs to be work we're all doing. After all, that's why they're here. Yet it's not uncommon for clinicians to feel they need to outsource all engagement around such issues to someone else.

Open Dialogue involves the creation of a space in which the client, together with whoever else is important to them, can start to open up about these things as a core aspect of their care. Creating trust is a crucial pre-requisite to this and I will write more about that in the next chapter but once that forms, a story that makes sense to them starts to emerge. It's not required to happen, but we are at least required to create the conditions in which it might.

Of the many families and networks I have worked with, almost every one reaches the point of "shall we say it?". They are wondering whether something – a deep and painful trauma – that has not been opened up about for years or even at all, needs now to be spoken about. This may be an experience of the person at the centre of care or someone else in the room, multiple people or even people they are

13

linked to who aren't in the room at all. Together they will start the process of adding it all up, connecting the dots and tracing it to what's happening to them now in the present moment. This, as I say, is a stage that almost everyone reaches.

In keeping with Open Dialogue, it should never be us, the clinicians, who answer the emerging questions. It is for them to decide when and how far they want to take it. But when it starts, you can really sense that the underlying cause is now being aired and, where possible, faced. To clean any wound you need to open it up first. The only difference in the emotional terrain, however, is that due to the intensity involved – often far more powerful than physical pain – it has to be the network's choice as to whether and how to open it.

The emphasis is always on creating a sense of agency for the network. It is they who are doing the work, we are just creating a safe space in which it can be done. But in order for us to be enable that agency we must first have it for ourselves. We must realise the power of our words and our presence and the way in which, as much as anything else, that is what really makes the difference. Medication can have an impact, especially in the short term, and it can therefore be needed, particularly in acute situations, but when it comes to the deeper underlying issues that led this family to sit before us in an acute mental health service setting, it is us – the clinicians working in true partnership together with the network – that are the real levers of change.

Starting The First Meeting

We set the tone before the first network meeting by asking who else would the client like to bring into the room. It's a question we spend a bit of time on, usually on the phone, to see if there are any friends or family members or others who they might want to join them. We explain that ours is an approach that involves working with everyone important to the person, rather than the person alone and so we encourage them to give this some thought. If it is a relative who is calling then we usually ask them to ask the person at the centre of concern who they might want to invite. Open Dialogue is not just about families – anyone can be invited; colleagues, neighbours, teachers, other professionals or healthcare providers outside the Open Dialogue team – anybody at all who is involved and might be useful. It is always the patient who has the final say, however, and sometimes they may choose to invite no one other than themselves. This is fine too. There are ways to still work systemically if there is only one person in the room. Such circumstances do not prevent us working dialogically. The way we do it in these situations is to hold a dialogue that tries to bring forth other voices nevertheless eg., "what would grandma say if she was in the room now?". This way we are always thinking together about systems and how what is happening can relate to these wider circles and influences.

The first meeting takes place at a mutually agreed time and usually as a home visit. This might be the same or next day if the crisis warrants it – just as is the case in our regular crisis home treatment teams – or a longer time window if that's agreeable or more useful too. The objective in that first meeting, however, is different in Open Dialogue. Rather than trying to arrive at a diagnosis and prescribe treatment as quickly as possible, our primary goal is to create a space where all the present voices can be heard and in order for that to happen we need to forge trusting relationships and do whatever we need to lay a firm foundation for that. We often forget that we have come into someone's life after many years of their own story, their own bonds and dynamics, and what is happening today is the culmination of all those events, relationships and intersections. What can we really and truly understand about them in just one hour? For this reason, humility is the key quality of an Open Dialogue practitioner. We are not there to be declarative or to dominate things at all. We are there to follow and support mutual learning, particularly for ourselves. That humility is what also helps a relationship to evolve as, in order to learn we need to listen, and when we really listen they start to trust. Numerous times my team and I have received this feedback at the end of a network meeting, "You guys really listened to me in a way that no one really has before."

But that sense of connection takes some effort to cultivate. The first hurdle is frequently the expectation of the network themselves. I often hear at the beginning of the meeting, "you're the doctor so tell me what's wrong with me." The idea of the all-knowing expert is one often propagated by society today but playing in to that can be the very thing that shuts down real dialogue. The minute a doctor or professional proclaims their learned opinion on a matter, any thoughts or perspectives others may have had are instantly squashed. As a result, my first response will tend to be something like, "Well, the experience you're having sounds very powerful and intense and it's clearly something you all know a lot more about. I haven't had this experience and so perhaps we could learn more from you all about it?" That tends to lead to a resumption of the dialogue.

Our strategy from the start is to help them to talk but to be as unobtrusive as possible in that process. As a result we have a standard question we tend to use in Open Dialogue at the start of the first meeting, namely, "What is the history of this meeting?" or variants of this such as, "What led to you calling/being referred to our service and attending this meeting today?". A lot of thought went into the design of that question as it is about as neutral and non-leading a question as you can ask.

Remember, our intention is to help them to take the meeting wherever they want to take it and so we need always to consider how best we can minimise our influence on it, specially at the very beginning.

Already you may be able to see here the difference with treatment as usual where the clinician taking charge and providing the answers is key. Stepping out of that role is a real culture shift and everyone goes through a process to bring that about. For the whole of our careers we have been conditioned to believe that we are the ones who will fix things. In a way it's a suit of armour, like a superhero outfit, that's hard to shed. If you think about it, however, you can draw a direct line between this approach and long term dependence on services. The more they feel they owe their recovery to you and need you to give them all the answers, the more they'll stick around. Our goal in all treatment approaches should be to help people stay out of services and move on with their lives. None of us would ever set out with the intention of creating chronic service dependence, yet too often that is what transpires. In Open Dialogue we suggest that is something to do with our own approach and this is why we put a lot of thought into exactly what we say and how we say it.

One of the reasons clinicians still, nevertheless, tend to dominate proceedings is because of how hard it can sometimes be to listen to the stories that come up. Some of them can be truly harrowing and so taking over the meeting is sometimes a way to regulate our own emotions, minimise the difficulty and distress felt by all, and "move on". The problem with that is that people can only really move on when they're ready. What they expect in those first encounters with services is to be heard. Often that's why they called. When I used to work as an in-patient consultant, hearing from patients many months after they had entered the system, they'd tell me how surprised they were about how little time was spent by professionals actually listening to them.

I have found that an investment of time to do this early on can pay huge dividends further down the line. And it is not just about time either. It's about our whole approach: how we listen, how we talk, how we act, how we respond.

At the start of an Open Dialogue meeting, as people speak, it is therefore vital that we genuinely have and show interest. A common way to do this is often to repeat the last words that were spoken. We don't paraphrase, we repeat directly. For students on our training this sometimes feels a little uncomfortable at first but usually, by the end of the training, they find they're doing it with their own families in their daily lives. It really does lead someone to feel and know they're being heard but you won't know it until you try it. So someone might say, "I don't really know how to start, it was a very hard time." To that you could respond, "Very hard time." You're not exactly asking a question here, you're just showing them you heard them and that you are right there with them. It's then for them to decide if they want to open up more or what to say next. Repeating the last words in the same way they said it makes them realise that you're listening without judgement or expectation and this often leads them to feel more comfortable and able to open up after that.

We also tell people not to be afraid to show their response to what's being said in their body language. The old advice to be like a mirror, or an immovable stone is never going to help us reach our primary goal, which is to build that relationship. Leaning forward at important points, showing your reaction in your face, not folding arms; all these things show that you're really listening and this is also the kind of thing you really can't fake. If you're doing it you almost certainly are listening.

It's important to remember also that we want to listen to everyone. The expression of multiple voices in the room is referred to as polyphony. Outer (or horizontal) polyphony refers to the different voices of different people in the room and inner (or vertical) polyphony are the different voices in a single person - we're not talking about hallucinations here (although that might be the case too), usually it's just about different perspectives. All of us can have multiple perspectives on a single issue. The aim in an Open Dialogue meeting is not to create harmony but to create polyphony. A demand for the former can often stifle the latter. If we all strive to reach a consensus then the dissenting voices will suddenly get pushed to one side.

When it comes to making plans, of course, there will be some need for agreement, but there's a way of doing that - with a particular emphasis in the plan to facilitate further dialogue – yet that is a matter for later. Much later. For now, all we need to focus on is polyphony. A tool we can use to bring this about is circular or relational questioning. Asking one person in the network how they felt hearing another speak is an example of this. A good way for polyphony to emerge is for a dialogue to ensue between the network and we often make an effort, again in a neutral way, without asking leading questions, to stimulate that. It's useful for the clinicians to remember that the meeting is about them not about us. The more the network members talk to each other, therefore, the more that is the case.

When this happens it can at times get quite heated. Things that have not been said before may start to emerge. Or the opposite may happen, with long silences emerging as if the words are in gestation, waiting to come out. In each such case it's hard for clinicians. Our tendency will be to try and regulate or damp things down or fill the spaces and terminate silences. In our training, we have found that the best way to help clinicians in resisting these longstanding impulses is to teach them some mindfulness.

Mark Hopfenbeck is another accomplished international Open Dialogue trainer who has taught it in more countries than I would actually even care to count. Both he and I have a longstanding experience as mindfulness teachers as well, so that has become a core element of the training we now provide together. Mindfulness helps us to notice our impulses as they emerge. That desire to step in and damp things down or gin things up, or the impulse to say something positive to take the pain away. We can't try and suppress all of this; that wouldn't be very healthy, dialogical or even practical. But nor do we want to act on them either. Instead, we can feel the words arising in our body. When I first started working in Open Dialogue I used to experience these impulses to step in on numerous occasions through the meeting as if they were protrusions emerging from my body like in the movie Donnie Darko. I would allow them and be present with them, but not try to excise them or expel them into words either, while keeping the centre of my attention on the person and family before me the whole time. This is the practice of presence with both myself and the network and it has a profound impact on the proceedings. In many ways it's analogous to what we do with the breath in meditation. We allow all our inner and outer experiences and perceptions to flow – noticing but not acting on them – while keeping the central focus of our attention on the breath the whole time. In a network meeting, as the clinician, we replace the breath with the client.

This is why we encourage the regular practice of mindfulness, or something similar, to all our students. Engaging daily in the act of quietly observing, without judgement, the myriad emotions, twists and turns in our own mind, helps us do the same with others too.

I truly believe that one of the key reasons our mental health system has adhered so stubbornly to working with individuals in isolation, instead of systemically with families and networks – despite multiple policy initiatives to encourage it over the years – is because of the emotional intensity involved in doing so. As human beings we will naturally opt for the path of least resistance, that which involves the least pain, and so we will default to seeing the individual without all the complications added by a network or group of people. The problem is that resisting this pain in the way we do only leads it to build and slowly store up over time and that's often why, in the end, so many of our patients just keep coming back. We're essentially putting a sticking plaster over a deep wound and hoping it'll go away. There's a reason most drug trials examine a timeline of only three to six months.

Creating a space where the underlying causes and experiences can emerge is, therefore, hard work. Even if the emotions aren't running high and the opposite happens, silences can feel intolerable too.

In Open Dialogue, however, we consider allowing silences (within reason of course) a good thing. I often feel when I'm sitting through a silence a sense of pressure in the room. But it is exactly this pressure that frequently then leads to a hitherto silent voice emerging. And when it does, I feel so glad that I kept my mouth shut.

All the way through, certainly until the last moments when we start to close the meeting, our plan is not to have a plan; to follow the conversation where it goes, to show physically that we're listening and only use our words where they help open things up more. "Can you say more about that?" is perhaps one of my most common questions in network meetings. All of this helps build their words, their dialogue and their narratives. And as they form, our own utterances can then use the same language. That way we're always attuned to their lead.

Another important dimension to open up into is the present moment. Anchoring what's being said to the here and now – how it feels right in this moment – is how we do that. "How do you feel now, after what you've said?" is therefore another common question.

It is important to bring in a caveat here, however, and that is that we can't force anything. We create opportunities for openness, that's all. Not mandates. We take the horse to water. It's up to the horse to do the drinking. The same applies at a meta level when we talk about the operationalisation of the model, but more on that later. Thankfully, in almost every case the opportunity is seized and that is because the very nature of a crisis is one in which things need to be said. What we call symptoms are really a form of language waiting to find words. As soon as we are willing to go beyond the professional gaze of "signs and symptoms" we will start to open the door to the world that lies beneath it.

All the way through our focus is thus on being attentive and creating spaces. And in so doing we build our relationship with the network. In the second half of the meeting we start to do some very concrete things to profoundly deepen this. For many, that's when some of the real power of the Open Dialogue approach comes to the fore.

Ending The First Meeting

The practice of reflection is one way in which Open Dialogue differs markedly from usual treatment. It's one of the main reasons we always need at least two clinicians in the room. Somewhere after the half way mark (though not necessarily, as it could easily be before that), when we have heard and absorbed some significant dialogue, we will tell the network that the colleagues in the room will now turn to and confer with one another. We will have a discussion about what we've heard so far and instead of doing this outside of the room – as is more common in standard treatment settings - we want to do it here in front of them. That way they can hear everything themselves and then tell us what they think. The first time usually requires a little explanation like this but after that it tends to flow easily and we can slip in and out of reflections whenever needed.

The purpose of the early reflections are really to show we were listening. We use their words as much as possible and speak about how that may have felt for us. We even talk about the reaction in the body, where we felt it and how it made us feel. This way they can really start to understand how deeply we were listening. The best reflections are personal, we might even self-disclose a little, if it feels right and appropriate, and share about something that may in someway resonate from our own life. What we try to avoid, however, is any form of interpretation or formulation. "clearly he felt that because..." or "I think what she really meant, when she said that was...". Our professional training often leaves us with analytical impulses and it can sometimes be hard not to voice them, but as with the impulses to interrupt, we can just be present with them. Feel that energy in the body. Don't push it away but don't act on it either, while in the meantime you focus on how that person actually feels and how, in some way, you were able to feel some of it too. Of course, you're not exactly the same and you haven't been on their journey, but your journey might mean that some of what was said will resonate in some way with you. This is your chance to say it.

It is at this time that another key aspect of systemic thinking can come to the fore and that's our awareness of what has come to be known over the years as the "social graces". It's actually an acronym with many more "g"s and "r"s and "a"s and "c"s and "e"s and "s"s in it, and it stands for the dimensions of our lives, often unseen, that nevertheless have a profound impact on us, our position in society, how we are listened to and the power we have within it. These are aspects like gender, geography, gender identity, race, age, culture, class, education, ethnicity and sexual orientation, among others. Each of these are elements that will also feed into the network meeting in terms of forces that are playing out in people's lives and how they relate to one another. A reflection can be a good moment to recognise this, specially if it in some way resonates with the clinician doing the reflection.

It is for this same reason also that we want a team that is as diverse as possible in terms of their own stories too. This is one of the reasons why we encourage, in the UK, all Open Dialogue teams to have peer workers within them. We thus refer to them as "Peer-supported Open Dialogue" teams to underscore the importance of that role. It makes a profound difference to the team's ability to relate to and resonate with others in the network when there is a person with their own lived experience – who is explicit about that – among us. Even if we can't have a peer worker in every network meeting, to have that voice in the team makes an enormous difference in our own team meetings. We recognise it as an expertise in its own right. One that is, in many respects, deeper than any expertise gained through study and qualifications and so, in my team for example, our peer worker colleague brings added layers of profound depth to our discussions and understandings. I'll elaborate more on these team meetings towards the end of the book too.

The reflection as a whole is thus a moment when the hierarchy starts to fade away. The network starts to realise that you're a human with feelings, just like them and what's more you're listening to them and sometimes feeling what they feel too. Now the barriers start to come down and the bonds between you start to cement. Using the right words – their words – and doing it in the right way, without judgement or any form of "expert" or clinical pose is therefore essential. After a while, this kind of discussion between colleagues in the room starts to feel more natural and we can intersperse the meeting with mini reflections after the first one. The important thing is for it to be as natural as possible. It's worth stressing, therefore, that you don't need to wait till the second half of the meeting to do it, if it feels right to come sooner, and in subsequent meetings it often will, go for it. Another thing is that we don't necessarily need to refer to it as a reflection at all; that way we avoid creating yet another piece of technical jargon. "My colleagues and I would like to have a chat…" is the way we might start to describe it.

When introducing this in our training we split our students into groups of three and ask them to practice reflections with one another several times before they go out and try it in the real world. One will speak about something mildly stressful in their lives at the moment while the other two listen and then, after a few minutes, the listeners will turn to one another and reflect on what they heard. The exercise is repeated three times so that each gets a turn to be the client. Sometimes the practice exercise doesn't go so well when the listener tries to analyse or interpret the person playing the client and this serves as a powerful learning exercise too as we realise how presumptive and jarring such things can sometimes feel. Usually that doesn't happen, however, as they retain the instruction to stick to what they heard, the language used and how it felt to them, empathically, to hear. The experience then is very different; an empowering and uplifting feeling of really having been heard. This exercise then helps people gain confidence before trying it out on families. And when they do, the feedback is frequently positive and profound. Reflections often help to cement a genuine bond – something both qualitatively and quantitatively different to what the clinicians were used to experiencing before – and that's when they come back to the next module fully fired up to learn more.

The reflection is all about forging a connection and, without doubt, those early reflections set the tone for the whole relationship you will have with the network going forward. The final aspect of the reflection is therefore always to ask them if they have any thoughts or responses to what you said. It is essential to do this as, even though you turn away from the network to speak exclusively with your colleague and not make eye contact with the network during your reflection, it still forms part of the wider dialogue. The feedback is therefore their chance to join it.

You might have several reflections during the course of the meeting and usually there will be one towards the end too. Again, they are all opportunities to demonstrate your humility. In this respect another core principle of Open Dialogue is evidenced, namely tolerating uncertainty. Tolerating uncertainty means not rushing in with an assessment or a conclusion. We like to think that, after listening to someone for an hour or so we can come to an overarching conclusion about everything that's going on, but can we really? In my experience the most respected clinicians are those who are most honest about this, in other words those who are most humble. For a couple of years I worked as a medical member of Mental Health Act review tribunals. This is where people admitted to hospital under a section – a legal mandate – get to appeal that decision. I would go from hospital to hospital, Trust to Trust, listening to clinicians talking about their patients and the care they provided, and I consistently found that the psychiatrists who, despite the circumstances, maintained the best relationship with their clients, were those who came across as most humble. Those who were honest about the fact that they didn't have it all figured out and were still just getting to know him or her – sometimes even after years of working with them.

Think about it - has a family member ever surprised you? Someone you have known for most or all of your life? Have you even surprised yourself? Done something that some time ago you may not have predicted? If that's the case then how certain can you be about someone you've only ever met a handful of times? Or maybe just once? There is a huge amount of uncertainty we walk around with in every day life, specially when it comes to human behaviour, and this is a reality that we don't want to just paper over in Open Dialogue. Be open about the fact that you're always learning. And that's why the dialogue is so important. Spending more time listening than talking.

Our reflections are a way of demonstrating that this is a relationship of equals and so trying to avoid that expert stance, wherever possible, is essential. We can be open about the fact that, in reality, we are always learning. This applies specially to any temptations we might have to slip into the paradigm of clinical certainties. Anyone who has worked in the mental health system for more than a couple of years will have plenty of experience of patients' diagnoses changing over and over again. And, again, those doctors most respected in tribunals were the ones who were most honest about that. They would say, "well, he has been given a diagnosis of... but to be honest it's debatable." We have to, of course, record diagnoses for the system from day one, as there would be no service otherwise – and we need to be honest about the necessity for that – but if that one or two words was the entirety of our definition and conclusion about what we were hearing then in a flash we would have removed the whole of that network's capacity to forge an understanding and a language that's meaningful to them. Instead of us helping them to find their own meaning, they would instead be reliant on ours. And from that point forward they would be forever dependent on us to understand what's happening with them. That's why, while we may use the diagnostic categories for our recording systems and some modes of communication, we don't use it as the organising principle of our dialogue. To be genuinely therapeutic, the true meaning and understanding of the experience unfolding is one that needs to arise from the network.

After all, if we didn't allow for that, what we are effectively telling them is that the only valid way to understand themselves is through the world of our technical expertise. It should be no surprise, therefore, if after that they always feel the need to return to our services for our help and guidance for the rest of their lives. And the same can happen when we talk of symptoms rather than actual experiences.

Symptoms are the core of the clinical lens that has become ingrained in many of us over the years. It's a template we have been repeatedly taught to apply to anything we hear and, like a radar, it's constantly scanning what comes through our ears for matches. Unfortunately, when this happens, we can't be fully listening. We are often not, as a result, attentively following the thread and nuances of the dialogue and what's being said. Over the years, surveys by the Care Quality Commission – the regulator of healthcare providers in the U.K. - have repeatedly found that, when asked about their care, users of mental health services consistently report, in significant majorities that, "mental health services do not always help me with what is important to me"[8]. The survey is sent to over 10,000 service users from 52 Trusts across the country and every year more than half report negatively on this metric and others like it. They are saying that their priorities – their thoughts and feelings about what they cared most about - were never fully heard. This almost certainly relates to the fact that in our traditional way of working, our objective is chasing symptoms – looking to know their diagnosis, rather than the

[8] *Care Quality Commission 2017 Community Mental Health Survey Statistical Release.* November 2017

actual person and story before us. How can we know what's really important to them at this moment in time, when it was never really a priority for us to do so?

This again is therefore where mindfulness comes in. By being mindful and paying attention to these urges to direct and cherry pick the conversation, we can actually find a way to focus the centre of our attention on the network. We can realise that, on the one hand, we have these reflexes to intervene of our own, which are perfectly understandable given our background, but at the same time our main task is to really be there for the network and we do this by being led by them. We can appreciate that because of the years of our training we will have our symptom radar going in the background - we can't suppress or wish that away - however, we can mindfully notice that too. We don't have to act on it, just notice it within us, maybe the feeling it evokes in our body as we resist the temptation to put those glasses on, while the whole time, we also ensure the centre of our attention is on the patient and the network.

We are not saying that these constructs are entirely useless. What we are saying, however, is that they can powerfully obstruct the space for genuine self-generated understandings to emerge from a network if we as clinicians routinely only comprehend or communicate through them.

In a dialogical approach we are not fishing or judging or concluding, we are simply opening. And when we do that, what is really important to the network starts to emerge. Surveys show that people who have had a major mental health diagnosis rate the importance of a spiritual life far more commonly than the rest of the public[9]. As a result, when we allow the network to occupy the space with what's important to them, spiritual notions and ideas might start to emerge. Although traditionally we are officially encouraged to be open to a client's spiritual life, in practice, when it arises to a significant degree in a clinical scenario there is often a tendency to minimise, ignore or even pathologise this on the part

[9] King et al., *Religion, Spirituality and Mental Health; Results From a National Study of English Households.* British Journal of Psychiatry, November 2012

of clinicians. In Open Dialogue, our first instinct however is to welcome it. If it is something the client is passionate about - and maybe the network too – then it's important to us as well. We want to learn more from a position of genuine curiosity, rather than judgement or interpretation. Many people understand their suffering through a spiritual lens. It's a worldview that makes sense to them and can often be a source of support and comfort. If it helps them in any way, then who are we to overtly or covertly dismiss it? Indeed there might be ideas that spring from that in terms of what might help and, again, unless they are obviously and overtly harmful, they should be welcomed too. It all helps us maintain our humility and that in turn helps us achieve our fundamental therapeutic goal, which is to build a sense of agency. And the first step to that is to ensure that every voice is heard.

When we allow ourselves to keep the space for dialogue patent, therefore, we find that we can learn so much more. In my experience, and that of virtually all of my team colleagues, this ends up being more than we had ever heard or learnt in our clinical work before. Indeed, the degree of revelation often takes clinicians aback. And by doing this, following the story that emerges rather than leading, guiding, categorising or interrupting it, we will start to notice how what we had formally described as symptoms start to make sense in the context of events that preceded it. It's a logical consequence.

We might be talking about traumas or other stressful encounters, dynamics or life events and the understandings might involve aspects of culture or spirituality, either way, by creating such a space an understanding will usually start to emerge and maybe even a way forward too. We can then take that lead and discuss it further in our reflections.

The final reflections are then further opportunities to demonstrate humility in that, unless imminent risk is involved (which we will address in the next chapter), it will be a time to make some suggestions about the next step. However, we will tend to do this tentatively, wondering to a colleague about it, instead of telling the network directly, "right, what we need to do is...". This will enable them to then decide what or how much of what we have said makes sense to them and thus what they'll proceed with. This is a crucial moment, therefore, in our mission to cultivate a sense of agency.

Having said this, easily the most common reflection I make towards the end of the meeting about next steps is "I wonder if it would be worth us having another of these meetings to continue the dialogue?". Usually the family is grateful to hear that this is possible and they can resume along the same lines with the same people (not a whole new set of folk as might often happen in treatment as usual, specially in crisis). A palpable sense of relief pervades the room when this is suggested and so when we take this back to them for their response on our reflection, they will often be happy to start thinking through with us the logistics of the next meeting.

This is when, as we come to a close, all the diaries come out to pin down a time for the next day and date. The family always understands when a clinician needs to guide them as to his/her availability as, again, seeing the same person and not having to repeat the whole story starts to feel important by this stage. This is why this can be a stage of deliberation as we negotiate our diaries together. It's worth noting here that no one in the team is being asked to work overtime to make these meetings happen. Though the length of the meetings might be more than we're used to, the number of meetings in the crisis stage are often fewer as they're happy to wait, in most cases, for another longer meeting like this and because of the meeting they feel safer to do that. If the crisis is sufficiently severe, however, we should be able to come or make contact again in the next day or two if needed.

As before, who attends the next meeting is the patient's call. For resource reasons a doctor won't be able to attend all meetings so, as long as they've been to a relatively early one, they can drop into a future network meeting for anyone in their team when needed.

Managing Risk Through Reflection

A common misperception about Open Dialogue is that there is little or no provision for the assessment and management of risk. In my experience, the exact opposite is the case. By allowing the space for people to speak in a relatively uninhibited way, a great deal more information often arises that would otherwise have been the case. I have very often heard things that, by the speaker's own admission, have never been expressed before to any professional. This degree of revelation was a unique experience for me in my early network meetings and it was one shared by every one of my colleagues.

This seemed to happen despite the fact that the individual concerned had often been in services for many years. Now we are used to hearing it all the time. As a result, we almost always have more than enough to complete our full risk assessment forms when we return to the office and if we don't we can always ask, while being explicit about why we need to ask.

Though all this information is gleaned usually without direct questioning – merely allowing the dialogue to flow – if needed, we can do this too. In fact, in Open Dialogue up to a third of all our time can be spent asking direct questions about anything that might be of particular interest or concern to us, but in my experience this is rarely needed. As I say, it usually all comes out in the dialogue.

If the information that we hear is, however, of particular concern to us – say we are worried about safety for someone – then another key difference in Open Dialogue is that we reflect about it in the meeting. Previously my practice used to be to discuss it with colleagues separately and make decisions outside the room, but not anymore. Colleagues and I turn to each other for a reflection and openly express the concerns we might have. This usually tends to be towards the end of the meeting and there will usually be some back and forth about it between the colleagues in the room, all heard by the network. It requires us to be honest but respectful and considerate the whole time too. It requires some skill and effort but it's an effort worth making as, otherwise, we will end up feeling compelled to make conclusions and decisions outside the meeting and suddenly all the opportunity to engage and empower the family will have been lost. Only where it is obviously risky not to do so will we take the discussion outside. I think I can count two examples over the last four years in my full time clinical work where this needed to happen.

One of the key benefits of doing it this way is that we can explore how valid our anxiety is. Sometimes we take draconian or restrictive actions due to our own subjective anxieties, rather than any risk that is actually present in the here and now. Humbly wondering aloud to a colleague will help us test our concerns before making any decision to proceed. Once we discuss this - including any emergency actions that we may be thinking about – we will ask the network to respond. Often they will think of solutions or provide reassurances that improve the situation there and then and suddenly the whole tone will have changed.

Discussing things openly in this way keeps us real. We are being authentic humans rather than virtual Gods who have a profound power over their liberty and freedoms. What they get to hear is our own concern, anguish and sometimes uncertainty, this way even if we have to take the most extreme step of deploying the Mental Health Act – which I have done in Open Dialogue settings several times – the relationship is nevertheless maintained. They knew you didn't arrive at the decision lightly and it wasn't what you really wanted to do, so the most important ingredient of care – trust - remains.

Of course, short of using such powers there are many other direct things that you can do if you're concerned about risk, like leaving emergency and out of hours contact details and organising 1:1 meetings, say with a key worker or care coordinator, before the next network meeting. There are often many contacts between network meetings so don't be afraid to offer them. Note, however, that unless it is a case where we feel we need to respond to an imminent risk (which is always rare), it is not for the clinician to assertively push such solutions on the network. It is the prerogative of the client, with support from their network, to guide and lead always.

Medication is also discussed in a similar vain. This is no longer our sole focus of treatment, the meetings are. But this does not mean that medication is not used. Multiple surveys over many years, however, show that patient preference is always for talking methods of treatment rather than medication[10]. Nevertheless, most people in standard care are

[10] McHugh et al. (2013), Patient preference for psychological vs pharmacologic treatment of psychiatric disorders: a meta-analytic review. Journal of Clinical Psychiatry, June 2013

prescribed medication as a first response. As a person-centred model of care, Open Dialogue gives the patient the space to consider what they really want and our role is to hear and respond to that. Given that medication based solutions are very much embedded as part of our health culture, the family will often ask about it relatively early on anyway. In such circumstances we might answer direct questions if they are asked in terms of options and side effects, but much of the pontification around medication options will take place during a reflection. Again, here being tentative and open about the lack of certainty when it comes to all things pharmacological helps. That way if a decision is made to take meds it will be theirs alone and so much more likely to be taken if that is the preference.

Other options are also brought up at this juncture, again usually led by the network, and this might include anything from 1:1 psychology to OT and Social Work input or even engagement with natural remedies or spiritual considerations too. As with medication, dialogue and reflection concerning everything that arises is important. This approach to treatment planning is what makes Open Dialogue such a flexible way of working. The number of permutations that can arise from a clinical meeting like this, where the clinicians aren't pushing an agenda but are open to all possibilities, are far greater. That is why flexibility in attitude and provision is considered a core principle of Open Dialogue. It's what we refer to as need-adapted.

In order to see it through, however, and deliver the whole of care in accordance with this approach, not just one meeting, there needs to be a wider system change. Open Dialogue is both a therapeutic modality and a model of care. As a result, wider operational considerations are also crucial to its implementation and this is what we will address in the next chapter.

Organising Open Dialogue

The first important operational aspect of Open Dialogue is that there are always two or more clinicians in network meetings. This doesn't mean 1:1 meetings can't happen. As mentioned above, this is fine too and can happen for many different reasons with a range of different professionals. Flexibility is a core guiding principle of the system; a flexibility that is guided by the network. When the network meets, however, we always need more than one clinician so that they can reflect with each other. If you think about it, there are often a multitude of clinical staff engaged with a family at any one time; the care coordinator, the psychiatrist, a psychologist, perhaps a support worker and maybe a social worker too. Open Dialogue simply asks all of these people to come together. In the first couple of meetings we try to involve most of those who will be involved in the care and that way we can ensure that we won't be introducing new people further down the line. Those clinicians then become part of the network over time. There is usually a core couple who tend to go to most network meetings and medics and others will then tend to come in and out if/when needed.

The major challenge around this happens when a patient switches from one team to another. In the UK, the number of teams a person might be assigned to has been proliferating in recent years. When I worked as a consultant in PICU – Psychiatric Intensive Care Unit, where people come if they have been violent on the general adult wards - I saw many people who had been under several teams - with a wholly different set of nurses, medics and other staff - in the last year and sometimes even the last month! How on earth could that be good for the development of therapeutic relationships? And when in crisis, people could easily end up seeing a different member of staff every day of the week; all strangers to the client and all needing him/her to retell their story anew every time.

That's why in Open Dialogue we emphasise consistency. Our aim is to ensure the same clinicians nearly always present and to make any boundaries between teams a lot more porous so that, together, the staff present can work more like a joined up unit. There are different ways of doing this but it tends to involve constructing the service around the patient rather than the other way round. This actually happens on a case by case basis in terms of how we respond to a crisis.

Crisis is usually the entry point to Open Dialogue care in the UK teams that are now running and when someone is taken on for crisis care – where an urgent response is required from mental health services due to the severity of the presentation - instead of only having the Crisis/Home Treatment Team members seeing them alone, we have staff from the longer term community mental health/recovery team join them, including a doctor, in one of the first meetings too. This way the relevant community team and crisis team members come together to work as a unified team with the network from the first week. And those same people largely stay together with them throughout their care thereafter.

Once the crisis is over they may see less of the crisis staff and more of the community staff, but there remains flexibility around this. There are no abrupt transition points and the family have a major say in who attends all the time.

This level of joint working is always something that senior Trust and NHS managers say they want but it is often obstructed by the implementation of hard borders between the teams where one set of professionals needs to abruptly pull out and be replaced by another. For Open Dialogue to operate, either these teams need to be fully integrated into a single team or at least they need to work jointly with families in a way that, to the family themselves, it all seems like one team working together the whole time.

Either way what we want is continuity of care. This needs to prevent, as much as possible, wholly new people being added to the network weeks, months or years down the line. The network that is forged in a crisis becomes like a stable organism, with its own system and parts. That then needs to be the backbone of care for the whole care pathway. Other 1:1 work can go on around it but all things need to converge in that space.

If a particular specialist - knowledgeable in a specific area or psychological intervention - is asked for by the network later on, then a person could be added to the network in those circumstances; ie. at the request of the family/friends and patient in the network. This is very different to additional professionals being added or switched because the "system" requires it.

You can see, therefore, how the culture shift in Open Dialogue is as much one for management as it is for clinicians. Understanding that services need to be wholly flexible and responsive, with decisions on which staff go where being taken as much as possible by the service users and their networks on the ground, on a case by case basis, is quite a paradigm shift. But if we are really serious about patient-centred care, it's essential.

Furthermore, our commitment to patient-centred care doesn't end at point of discharge either. In Open Dialogue we have what's called an "Open Door Discharge Policy". This means that from the beginning the clinicians make clear that they're here to stay. Their relationship with the network is not a transient one and can carry on for as long as needed. Discharge, therefore, can be less threatening as we are clear that they can return anytime straight back to the team – no need to go through the GP or other assessment hoops or services – just call our number. And when they do we will endeavour to ensure the same clinicians will work with them, wherever possible. That relationship is therefore again at the heart of our approach to discharge.

Contrary to how most services work, we actually encourage our families to come back. If they ever feel things are becoming a bit difficult we urge them to get in touch, not to wait till things really get out of hand or a full blown episode appears to be in play. We may then have a one off network meeting to discuss the issue at hand, or maybe a few or even return them formally to our caseload. Either way, we'll approach what ever is happening together. It is because of the relationship we have taken the time to cultivate, that this becomes possible. There is a welcoming return, rather than an active avoidance. The network doesn't have to feel guilty or awkward about calling us up and both the family and the clinicians feel comfortable when it happens. The beauty of this is that, in the longer term, it can then lead to less need and service use as a result. Just knowing that's there - and can be tapped occasionally when needed, even for relatively low level concerns - can make all the difference.

Clinicians engaged in a system like this that is focused on the relationship at its core have an entirely different experience of their work as well. I know members of my own team who would have long since moved on or retired by now if it wasn't for the profound relationships that working this way and this consistently with families has brought about. Over time, you start to feel a part of the network. Rather than being outside power brokers swooping into their lives, we are welcomed like kin into their homes to join a conversation among equals.

Once the hierarchy is more flattened in this way the nature of the meetings themselves can change somewhat. In the early days the emphasis is very much on creating a space that the network can fill with the clinicians confining their dialogue to reflections in the main. After a few meetings, however, clinicians will find themselves more naturally able to engage in friendly banter. This isn't clinical or related to any kind of assessment but it's more a mutual back and forth about whatever subject has arisen. To the outside observer that might sound like a group of friends having a chat. All of this is fine as, underneath it all, you are deepening the relationship. Many network meetings will feel informal in this way as strong bonds develop. Don't be afraid to get on like that and enjoy your time in the network meetings. It all helps with your ability to really be there when difficult times and subjects emerge. The more they know you the more they can trust you.

A couple of days ago I was in a meeting where most of our time was spent discussing the joy of having small children — nurseries, birthdays, teething and the like — all prompted by the new-born who was the latest addition to our network that day. As a wider network we have been through a lot together, including hospitalisation of the person at the centre of it, and all of our light hearted talk that day was very much groundwork for any difficult times that may lay ahead and her ability to trust us and open up with us if and when they do.

As well as riffing more in this way in later network meetings, we also tend to open the meetings differently. There is no longer any point asking about the history of the meeting so instead we tend to ask, "how would you like to use the time?" or, "What would you like to talk about today?". This creates a space the network can then move to fill, whether that's spontaneous social chitchat or more serious issues that have arisen or something network members may have planned to bring up in advance.

It is this relationship that leads to families often opting to wait for the next network meeting, rather than – when in crisis – having more frequent visits with people they have never met before from the crisis team. Having less frequent contacts in crisis like this doesn't mean the distress is any less, it just means that the network meeting is helping build their resilience and self-reliance at the same time.

There may be a time when the family opt for a pause or even a cessation of network meetings and perhaps continue the care with more traditional 1:1 meetings for the time being. Sometimes our students make the mistake of thinking that's not acceptable in Open Dialogue, but it is. It is still Open Dialogue if network meetings pause at the request of the network, so long as it has been offered and it is their decision to stop and not that of the clinicians or "the system". I have seen this after a string of particularly emotive network meetings in which family members felt they'd like a pause and sometimes that pause has lasted a year or more before they decide to convene another one again. Open Dialogue is about the ability to have network meetings when needed, not to enforce them. More than anything else it is a need adapted approach and that means it is driven radically by the needs of the network, so we can adapt to almost anything. That is the common theme throughout; patient-centred at all times.

Another strong theme is the way in which we discuss the network. The way we talk about people is consistent whether or not network meetings are going on. What I am referring to here is a philosophy we describe as "nothing about us without us" – wherever possible only talking about people if they are in the room. This is a principle that is at the heart of how we organise our team, how we work together and how we talk to each other. We realise that how we behave, engage and react with our service users is as much about us and how we organise ourselves as it is about them. Realising and working with this is what teamwork in Open

Dialogue is all about and this is the subject of our final chapter.

Teamwork & Team Talk

In Open Dialogue we have regular team meetings, just like any other community team. The nature of the meeting, however, is different. Traditional meetings tend to involve the team discussing and dissecting a case, many team members will express a view as they pontificate together before decisions are collectively made about how to proceed. The clinicians involved are then despatched back to the client to carry out the team's instructions. From an Open Dialogue perspective there are many problems here. Firstly, the team discussions are taking place in a separate space with no involvement of the client or network concerned. In addition, people who have never met or connected with the family are then discussing and making decisions about them. When this happens, a member of staff might feel, over time, that they know and are familiar with a person or group of people they have never met. What they know, of course, is the image of that family rather than the family or person themselves. These images can quickly become caricatures. In the absence of any actual connection, the team start imagining what they are like, filling in the gaps with sometimes stereotypical notions of what they have come to expect from patients. All they have to go on is what they have known or seen before, rather than the actual people under discussion. Slipping into judgement about the family can happen easily under these circumstances too. Eye rolling may go on in the room, with words like "chaotic" and "nightmare" being uttered. This energy then affects the clinicians who are actually involved in the case and they then take that back to the family. Seeing them through this new, often subtly pejorative, lens their interactions will change somewhat. If nothing else, they may consider themselves to be even more of an expert on that person or persons since they last met and so impart their wisdom with more conviction than before. The conviction of the whole team. A team who never met them.

We can see here how the cultivation of relationship can be substantially impaired by this process and how any chance of building the family's sense of agency and control has been subdued too. A chasm may have developed as the family and their team now move on different tracks. There is evidence that this routinely happens in mental health services across the UK, with detrimental effect. As mentioned before, the Care Quality Commission's annual national survey of mental health services finds that the vast majority of service users reject the statement, "my team know what's important to me". The vast majority thus don't feel they have the kind of relationship they would like with their team — one in which they are truly heard and understood.

As a result, in Open Dialogue we conduct our team meetings entirely differently. We start with a few minutes of mindfulness, making sure we are grounding ourselves in the present moment before beginning. After that we then discuss business items (eg. specifics about someone's housing that we might need to complete a form for, or a driving license application one of us might need help with etc.). This business section can be at the end of the meeting too if the team prefers.

The main aspect of our meetings, however, are the reflections. Here two or more clinicians involved in a client's care will come to the front and face one another – ignoring the rest of the team. They will then have a reflective discussion about their mutual case. As the people in the reflection know the family very well, there is no need to bring up much by way of actual content of the case – they both know the story anyway - and besides, out of respect for the family, we want to steer clear of disclosing content unless we have to (eg. for reasons of risk that need to be discussed). What we focus on instead in these reflections is our own subjective experience. How are we feeling about what's going on and how we did and what emotions might be coming up for us in this case. We are aware of our own buttons, based on our own life stories (which we have each explored by looking at our genograms etc. in self-work exercises – more on that later), and how that might play into our reactions. In a lot of ways, therefore, the reflective discussion is about us and how we are doing. It's a form of support and, through it a self-exploration can ensue that will help inform the real dialogue about next steps or problems that may be arising with the network themselves. We are not here to solve problems but to understand them better and also understand our own perspectives better so we can then return to the family knowing better how we feel about things.

After that reflection is finished, the clinicians involved then turn to the rest of the team who then turn to each other – not looking back to the involved clinicians – in order to reflect among themselves about what they just heard. In a wholly dialogical way the remaining team members reflect with one another empathically, expressing what resonated with them and how they felt hearing their colleagues. A lot of validation often happens here as we have usually been in their shoes and can sometimes say a thing or two about how we reacted in those circumstances. At the end we then let the original clinicians reflect a final time themselves and usually they will feel heard and encouraged, with maybe new ideas evolving during the process. The aim is to give them the confidence to proceed with their own network.

What I have learnt over the years is that, in order for the people in our care to develop a sense of agency, the staff looking after them have to develop that first. They have to know that it is they who can usually make the difference and not anyone else, not technology or any experts outside or above them.

This collegiate, less hierarchical way of going about clinical discussions has come to be known in the UK NHS Open Dialogue community as "intervision". The word came from some Dutch teams who we trained and it's a contrast to the traditional notion of "supervision" where leaders are traditionally required to guide their underlings. Again, in cases where there is real concern around risk, some of that may need to happen too. The clinicians involved might seek direct advice from other members of the team like the medic or social worker and, in those circumstances, that is fine. Legal or pharmaceutical remedies might, for example, be needed and these discussions can take place to be actioned as needed thereafter as well. All this is, however, very much the exception to our usual proceedings.

Otherwise, our meetings are about ourselves as much as possible. They can be emotional and tears are occasionally shed as we open up with each other about our own experience – keeping it as subjective as we can – so we can be as helpful and non-blaming as we can with our own clients. We are looking after ourselves in this way and it is only by doing that, that we can then be there for others too. This path of self reflection is a fundamental component of Open Dialogue – both the training and the operation of the team. It starts in the first week of training under the heading of self-work.

Every Open Dialogue trainee engages in a significant amount of personal development. If you think about it, its remarkable that this doesn't happen as standard. To be a psychotherapist you need to have had years of your own therapy during training and then continue it regularly on an ongoing basis. In acute mental healthcare, however, where the levels of emotional distress and uncertainty can be far higher, no such requirement exists for most professionals. We are working in the world of emotions with no focus or active development of our own. What experience from our own childhood may be playing out before us in the dynamic we have with a particular service user? What aspect of someone's presentation might hit us particularly hard because of something that in some way mirrors our own lives or networks? How do the dynamics in a family resonate with some of our own and so affect the way we respond? Walking round completely ignorant of these things means that, at the very least, we're unable to give someone our best and, at worst, we may actually be inadvertently causing harm by our reactions. This is why self work is so important.

In every Open Dialogue training students are asked to do genograms – mapping and sharing their family tree with another team member and looking for patterns in things that have happened, experiences, events and reactions that may have repeated through the generations. By knowing your own system better you get to know yourself better, and all the forces that act upon you today. There are numerous other exercises that build on this like sharing a memento with a colleague – something meaningful that serves as a gateway to a discussion about an important moment or period in your life. We have dozens of exercises like this and engaging with them in the training is just the start. It is crucial that teams create spaces to engage in this on an ongoing basis. In my own team, one intervision a month is focused on self-work. We also have away days a couple of times a year and at least half of that time centres around self-work.

All of this then feeds in to the reflections we do in intervision, when we start to spot how our subjective reactions are also a factor of our own lives and stories. And these reflections then help us bring that same awareness into network meetings and, if it feels right and helpful, we might choose to reflect it there too. There is no barrier to this kind of self-disclosure in Open Dialogue, but it is not mandatory either. If it feels like it will help the network in that moment and you feel comfortable opening up then by all means do so.

These are also the moments – both in intervisions and network meetings – when I feel myself most inspired by our peer worker colleagues. They are able to share in a way that can make a profound difference and help lead the way for the rest of us too. I have seen numerous times in which the ability to say, "I have been there too. I may not be in that place right now, but I really do hear you", has led to a genuine opening and a profound shift in all of us – not just the client.

To me, this goes to the heart of Open Dialogue and the philosophy behind it. The desire to be an active agent for change is human nature and, moreover, it's particularly ingrained in those of us who choose to work in the caring professions. However, in the emotional realm, stepping forward ourselves to push or make that change happen, can be disabling to the person we're trying to help. It risks reinforcing an underlying belief in their own lack of capacity. Many times, in fact, all they really needed was someone to be there alongside them. This takes effort and training because we have to know ourselves better to appreciate the true depth of the connection we are experiencing in that moment and then we have to learn to be open to it – rather than push it away – and furthermore, to then demonstrate and communicate it to the person as well. But when we can do this and really show someone that we are genuinely alongside them and that we don't need or want anything else from them then, sometimes for the first time in their life, that's when they will genuinely feel heard. That's when the pain that lurked deep in a wound for many years can start to emerge and that's when their liberation can truly begin. Sure, sometimes they may need specific help in certain ways too, whether it be with housing and social support, medication, stays in hospital or anything else, but a space has opened. There is light at the end of the tunnel. And one day, if the time and circumstances are right, it might lead to a genuine recovery and the start of a new chapter in life.

I'll end the book with the words of Kirsty Lee, whose family was among one of the first to receive Open Dialogue in one of our U.K. pilot sites...

"If I could give one word for Open Dialogue, one word to those who are suffering mental health [difficulties], to those families facing fears and worry and blame for their loved ones, then that word would be hope. There is hope in Open Dialogue because Open Dialogue gave us hope."

Appendix: Exercise

The formal description of Open Dialogue consists of 7 Core Principles and 12 Key Elements. The Core Principles are overarching ideas that relate to both the operational and practice aspects of Open Dialogue, whereas the Key Elements refer exclusively to the clinical practice known as Dialogic Practice. They are all elaborated upon in the book and so a useful exercise can be to look back through it and locate and highlight the relevant sections for each.

Core Principles

1. Immediate Help – receiving a response from the service within a day (or a few days at the most in practice) in response to crisis.

2. Social Network Perspective – inviting the network to participate as partners in the process of care.

3. Flexibility And Mobility – a patient-centred, need-adapted approach that includes an openness to a variety of permutations of care that might arise from the dialogue that takes place in network meetings.

4. Responsibility – those engaged at the start of care will then take on the responsibility to organise it with and for the network.

5. Psychological Continuity – a commitment to maintain continuity of care with the same clinicians involved from the start continuing with the network throughout the episode of

care. Any referrals back into service will also engage the same clinicians wherever possible.

6. Tolerance Of Uncertainty – the fundamental attitude required of clinicians to facilitate dialogue and maintain an open space throughout.

7. Dialogue (& Polyphony) – the ultimate objective is to enable a dialogue where all voices can be heard.

Key Elements

The Key Elements elaborate upon the 2 Core Principles that are practice based - Tolerance of Uncertainty and Dialogue & Polyphony (particularly the latter). They represent the underlying therapeutic approach in Open Dialogue and the key elements describe what they entail in practical terms.

1. Two (or More) Therapists in the Team Meeting

2. Participation of Family and Network

3. Using Open-Ended Questions

4. Responding To Clients' Utterances

5. Emphasising the Present Moment

6. Eliciting Multiple Viewpoints

7. Use of a Relational Focus in the Dialogue

8. Responding to Problem Discourse or Behaviour in a Matter-of-Fact Style and

Attentive to Meanings

9. Emphasising the Clients' Own Words and Stories, Not Symptoms

10. Conversation Amongst Professionals (Reflections) in the Treatment Meetings

11. Being Transparent

12. Tolerating Uncertainty

Author Bio

Russell Razzaque trained originally at the Royal London Hospital Medical School and has been a Consultant Psychiatrist in the NHS since 2006. He has worked in a variety of settings in that role — crisis home treatment team, in-patient, PICU, drug services and community recovery teams — and currently works in a busy community recovery team in east London. He also worked as a tribunal doctor for several years and has been an Associate Medical Director of his NHS Trust too.

In addition he is currently Director of Research at his Trust and an Honorary Senior Lecturer at University

College, London as well as a Visiting Professor at London South Bank University.

He is also a mindfulness trainer and Open Dialogue trainer and he coordinates the first accredited Open Dialogue training in the NHS, which you can learn more about at www.apopendialogue.org

Printed in Great
Britain
by Amazon